COLLEGE LONDON

Cello
Scales, Arpeggios & Studies

for Trinity College London examinations
from 2007

Initial-Grade 8

Published by:
Trinity College London
89 Albert Embankment
London SE1 7TP UK

T +44 (0)20 7820 6100
F +44 (0)20 7820 6161
E music@trinitycollege.co.uk
www.trinitycollege.co.uk

Registered in the UK
Company no. 02683033
Charity no. 1014792

Printed in England by the Halstan Printing Group, Amersham, Bucks.

Examples of scale and arpeggio bowing patterns

The examples below are given as indications of bowing patterns for all instruments from the syllabus. Clefs, key and time signatures have been deliberately omitted in order not to imply an association with any one scale or member of the string family, or any particular interpretation or emphasis within each scale.

One octave scale, slurred in pairs

or

or (For Grade 1 only):

or

Two octave scale, slurred in pairs

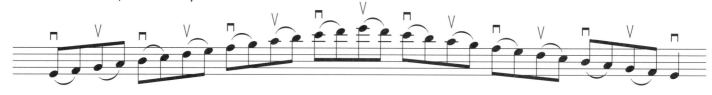

or

Scale slurred four notes to a bow

or

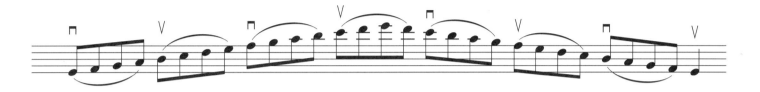

Scale slurred seven notes to a bow

etc.

or

etc.

Scale slurred three notes to a bow

etc.

Arpeggio slurred in pairs

or

Arpeggio of a 7th slurred in pairs

Arpeggio slurred three notes to a bow (one octave)

Arpeggio slurred three notes to a bow (two octaves)

Initial

Scales (all from memory):

The following scales to be performed with the indicated rhythmic patterns on each note:

C major scale (one octave)

G major scale (one octave)

D major scale (one octave)

Grade 1

Candidate to prepare the Bowing Exercise and then *either* Section i) *or* Section ii) in full.

Bowing Exercise (from memory):

The candidate will be asked to play one scale of their own choice from any of those listed below for Grade 1.
The scale should be played with two separate crotchets on each degree of the scale, one down bow and one up bow.
For example:

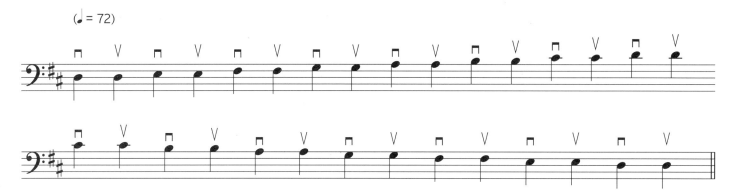

Section i) Scales and Arpeggios and Technical Exercise (all from memory):

The following scales and arpeggios to be prepared.

When the examiner requests a key, the candidate should play the scale and then, immediately (or after a moment's pause), the arpeggio.

Scales to be played with separate bows *and* slurred in pairs, as requested by the examiner. Arpeggios to be played with separate bows only.

See pages 2-4 for rhythmic and bowing patterns.

C major scale (two octaves)

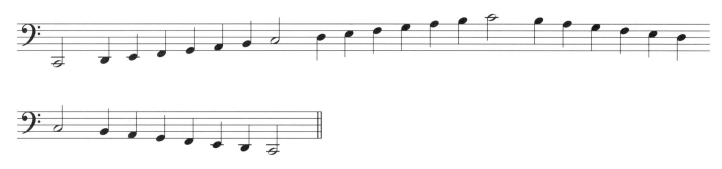

C major arpeggio (two octaves)

D major scale (one octave)

D major arpeggio (one octave)

G major scale (one octave)

G major arpeggio (one octave)

G minor (to the 5th, scale only)

Technical Exercise (from memory):

Double Stops (open strings)

Grade 1 continued

or Section ii) Studies:

Candidate to prepare the following three studies and to choose one of them to play first. The examiner will then select one of the remaining studies to be performed:

1. Marching On!

2. Procession

3. Gliding in a Clear Blue Sky

Grade 2

Candidate to prepare the Bowing Exercise and then *either* Section i) *or* Section ii) in full.

Bowing Exercise (from memory):

The candidate will be asked to play one scale of their own choice from any of those listed below for Grade 2.
The scale should be played with the rhythm ♩ ♫ on each degree of the scale, separate bows.
For example:

Section i) Scales and Arpeggios and Technical Exercise (all from memory):

The following scales and arpeggios to be prepared.

When the examiner requests a key, the candidate should play the scale and then, immediately (or after a moment's pause), the arpeggio.

Each scale/arpeggio pair to be played with separate bows *or* slurred in pairs, as requested by the examiner.

Minor scale to be played in *either* natural *or* harmonic *or* melodic form, at candidate's choice.

See pages 2-4 for rhythmic and bowing patterns.

C major scale (two octaves)

C major arpeggio (two octaves)

A major scale (one octave)

A major arpeggio (one octave)

Grade 2 continued

F major scale (one octave)

F major arpeggio (one octave)

Bb major scale (one octave)

Bb major arpeggio (one octave)

G natural minor scale (one octave)

or

G harmonic minor scale (one octave)

or

G melodic minor scale (one octave)

G minor arpeggio (one octave)

Technical Exercise (from memory):

The following exercise to be performed in the pattern shown, starting on G, D *and* C strings:

Double Stops (fifths and sixths):

or Section ii) Studies:

Candidate to prepare the following three studies and to choose one of them to play first. The examiner will then select one of the remaining studies to be performed:

1. Waltz

Grade 2 continued

2. Morris Dance

3. Barcarolle

Grade 3

Candidate to prepare the Bowing Exercise and then *either* Section i) *or* Section ii) in full:

Bowing Exercise (from memory):

The candidate will be asked to play one scale of their own choice from any of those listed below for Grade 3. The scale should be played with eight semiquavers on each degree of the scale, as in the following example given below in G major:

Section i) Scales and Arpeggios and Technical Exercises (all from memory):

The following scales and arpeggios to be prepared.

When the examiner requests a key, the candidate should play the scale and then, immediately (or after a moment's pause), the arpeggio.

Minor scales to be played in *either* melodic *or* harmonic form, at candidate's choice.

Scales to be prepared with separate bows *and* slurred in pairs.

Arpeggios to be prepared with separate notes *and* slurred three notes to a bow.

Dominant 7ths to be prepared with separate bows *and* slurred two notes to a bow.

See pages 2-4 for rhythmic and bowing patterns.

G major scale (two octaves)

G major arpeggio (two octaves)

D major scale (two octaves)

D major arpeggio (two octaves)

F major scale (two octaves)

Grade 3 continued

F major arpeggio (two octaves)

E♭ major scale (one octave, starting on the C string)

E♭ major arpeggio (one octave, starting on the C string)

D melodic minor scale (two octaves)

or

D harmonic minor scale (two octaves)

D minor arpeggio (two octaves)

Dominant 7th in the key of C (one octave, starting on open G)

Dominant 7th in the key of G (one octave, starting on 1st finger D on the C string)

Technical Exercises (from memory):

a) Chromatic Phrase:

to be performed with separate bows:

b) Double Stops (fifths, sixths and octaves):

The following exercise to be performed in the pattern shown starting on the open G, D *and* C strings:

or Section ii) Studies:

Candidate to prepare the following three studies and to choose one of them to play first. The examiner will then select one of the remaining studies to be performed:

1. Andantino

Grade 3 continued

2. Minuetto

Gently flowing

3. Tango

Molto ritmico

Grade 4

Candidate to prepare the Bowing Exercise and then *either* Section i) *or* Section ii) in full.

Bowing Exercise (from memory):

The candidate will be asked to play one scale of their own choice from any of those listed below for Grade 4. The scale should be played with the rhythm ♩. ♪ ♩ on each degree of the scale, as in the following example given below in A major:

Section i) Scales and Arpeggios and Technical Exercise (all from memory):

The following scales and arpeggios to be prepared.

When the examiner requests a key, the candidate should play the scale and then, immediately (or after a moment's pause), the arpeggio.

Minor scales to be played in *either* melodic *or* harmonic form, at candidate's choice.

All scales to be prepared with separate bows *and* slurred four notes to a bow.

All arpeggios to be prepared with separate bows *and* slurred three notes to a bow.

Dominant 7ths to be prepared with separate bows *and* slurred in pairs.

Chromatic scale to be prepared with separate bows only.

See pages 2-4 for rhythmic and bowing patterns.

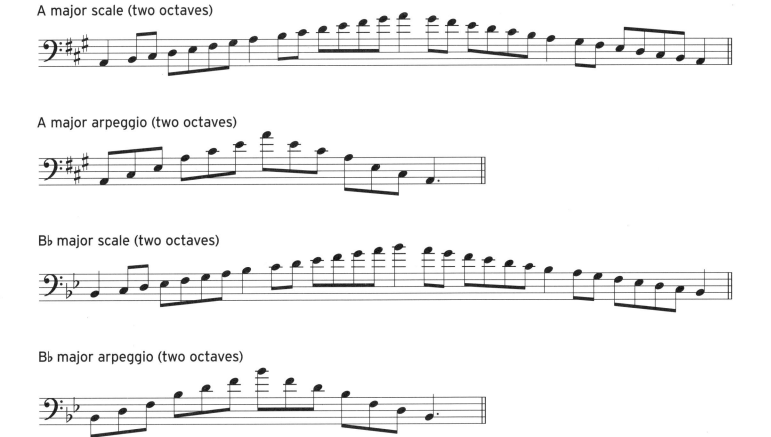

A major scale (two octaves)

A major arpeggio (two octaves)

B♭ major scale (two octaves)

B♭ major arpeggio (two octaves)

Grade 4 continued

Eb major scale (two octaves)

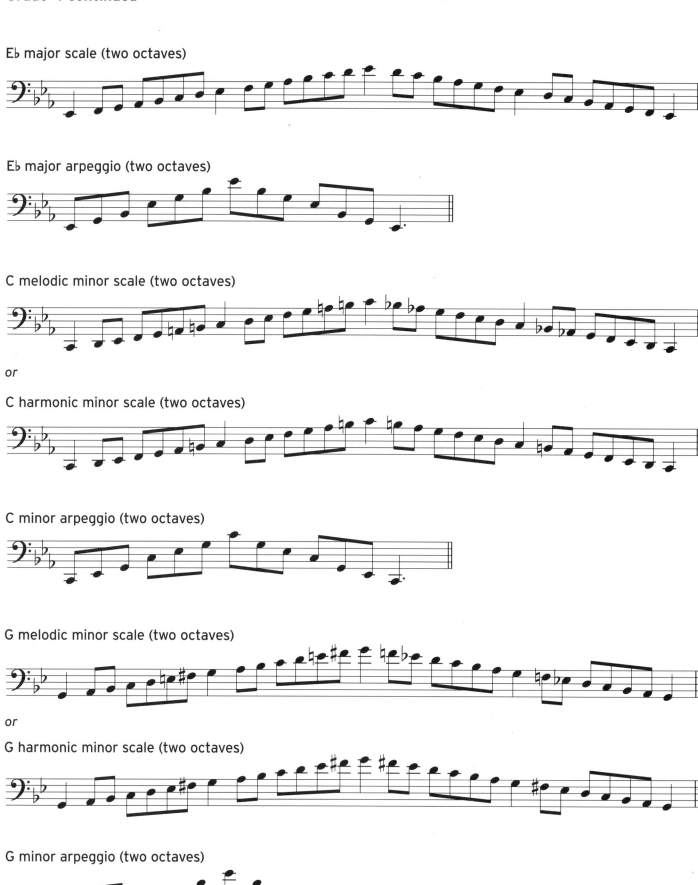

Eb major arpeggio (two octaves)

C melodic minor scale (two octaves)

or

C harmonic minor scale (two octaves)

C minor arpeggio (two octaves)

G melodic minor scale (two octaves)

or

G harmonic minor scale (two octaves)

G minor arpeggio (two octaves)

Dominant 7th in the key of F (two octaves, starting on open C)

Dominant 7th in the key of G (two octaves, starting on 1st finger D on the C string)

Dominant 7th in the key of E♭ (one octave, starting on B♭)

Chromatic scale starting on open G (one octave)

Technical Exercise (from memory):

Double Stops (octaves and sixths):

The following exercise to be performed in the pattern shown, starting on the open G, D and C strings:

(♩ = c.100)

Grade 4 continued

or Section ii) Studies:

Candidate to prepare the following three studies and to choose one of them to play first. The examiner will then select one of the remaining studies to be performed:

1. Elegy

2. Shanty

3. Polonaise

Allegro energico

Grade 5

Candidate to prepare the Bowing Exercise and then *either* Section i) *or* Section ii) in full.

Bowing Exercise (from memory):

The candidate will be asked to play one scale of their own choice from any of those listed below for Grade 5. The scale should be played with a martelé* bow stroke. (♩ = 88)

Section i) Scales and Arpeggios and Technical Exercise (all from memory):

The following scales and arpeggios to be prepared.

When the examiner requests a key, the candidate should play the scale and then, immediately (or after a moment's pause), the arpeggio.

Minor scales to be played in *either* melodic *or* harmonic form, at candidate's choice.

All scales to be prepared with separate bows *and* slurred four notes to a bow except for the thumb position scale (to be prepared with a down and an up bow on each note).

All arpeggios to be prepared with separate bows *and* slurred three notes to a bow.

Chromatic scales to be prepared with separate bows *and* slurred four notes to a bow.

Dominant 7ths to be prepared with separate bows *and* slurred four notes to a bow.

Diminished 7th to be prepared with separate bows only.

See pages 2-4 for rhythmic and bowing patterns.

C major scale (three octaves)

C major arpeggio (three octaves)

E major scale (two octaves)

*Martelé:** Immediately after the initial 'bite' or pressure accent the pressure must be released. The bow moves quickly but does not leave the string. Each stroke should end before applying pressure for the 'bite' at the start of the new stroke. This will result in an inevitable small silence between each note.

E major arpeggio (two octaves)

Ab major scale (two octaves)

Ab major arpeggio (two octaves)

A melodic minor scale (two octaves)

or

A harmonic minor scale (two octaves)

A minor arpeggio (two octaves)

E melodic minor scale (two octaves)

or

E harmonic minor scale (two octaves)

Grade 5 continued

E minor arpeggio (two octaves)

D major scale (one octave, in thumb position starting on the D string)

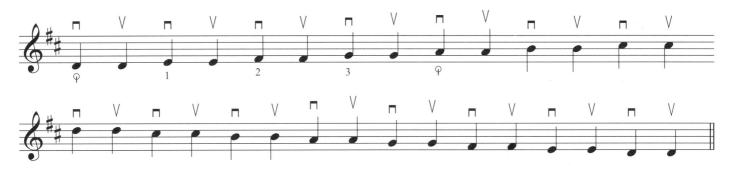

Dominant 7th in the key of F (two octaves, starting on C)

Dominant 7th in the key of G (two octaves, starting on D)

Chromatic scale starting on C (two octaves)

Chromatic scale starting on D (two octaves)

Diminished 7th starting on A, 1st finger on the G string (one octave)

Technical Exercise (from memory):

Double Stops (octaves, sixths and thirds):

The following exercise to be performed in the pattern shown, starting on the open G, D *and* C strings:

Grade 5 continued

or Section ii) Studies:

Candidate to prepare the following three studies and to choose one of them to play first. The examiner will then select one of the remaining studies to be performed:

1. Jig

2. Arioso

3. Habañera

Grade 6

Candidate to prepare the Bowing Exercise and then *either* Section i) *or* Section ii) in full.

Bowing Exercise (from memory):

The candidate will be asked to play one scale of their own choice from any of those listed below for Grade 6. Each note of the scale should be played as two spiccato* quavers. (♩ = 132)

Section i) Scales and Arpeggios and Technical Exercise (all from memory):

The candidate should prepare major and minor scales and arpeggios from Group 1 *or* Group 2. Additionally, **all** candidates should prepare the thumb position scale, chromatic scales, diminished 7th arpeggios and technical exercise listed on page 34.

When the examiner requests a major tonal centre, the candidate should play in succession:
>The major scale
>The major arpeggio
>The dominant 7th starting on that note and resolving onto the tonic (two octaves)

When the examiner requests a minor tonal centre, the candidate should play in succession:
>The melodic minor scale
>The harmonic minor scale
>The minor arpeggio

The candidate may pause briefly between individual scales and arpeggios.

All scales to be prepared with separate bows *and* slurred four notes to a bow, except D major scale in thumb position (to be prepared with separate bows only).

All arpeggios to be prepared with separate bows *and* slurred three notes to a bow.

Dominant 7ths to be prepared with separate bows *and* slurred four notes to a bow.

Chromatic scales to be prepared with separate bows *and* slurred four notes to a bow.

Diminished 7ths to be prepared with separate bows *and* slurred four notes to a bow.

See pages 2-4 for rhythmic and bowing patterns.

Group 1 – C, B, E♭ tonal centres:

C major scale (three octaves)

C major arpeggio (three octaves)

*Spiccato: the bow starts off the string and leaves the string after every note, creating a small 'saucer' or 'smile' shape over the string, touching the string at the lowest point of the 'saucer' or 'smile' shape.

Dominant 7th in the key of F, starting on C (two octaves)

C melodic minor scale (three octaves)

C harmonic minor scale (three octaves)

C minor arpeggio (three octaves)

B major scale (two octaves)

B major arpeggio (two octaves)

Grade 6 continued

Dominant 7th in the key of E, starting on B (two octaves)

B melodic minor scale (two octaves)

B harmonic minor scale (two octaves)

B minor arpeggio (two octaves)

E♭ major scale (two octaves)

E♭ major arpeggio (two octaves)

Dominant 7th in the key of A♭, starting on E♭ (two octaves)

E♭ melodic minor scale (two octaves)

Eb harmonic minor scale (two octaves)

Eb minor arpeggio (two octaves)

or

Group 2 – D, F, G#/Ab tonal centres:

D major scale (three octaves)

D major arpeggio (three octaves)

Dominant 7th in the key of G, starting on D (two octaves)

D melodic minor scale (three octaves)

Grade 6 continued

D harmonic minor scale (three octaves)

D minor arpeggio (three octaves)

F major scale (two octaves)

F major arpeggio (two octaves)

Dominant 7th in the key of B♭, starting on F (two octaves)

F melodic minor scale (two octaves)

F harmonic minor scale (two octaves)

F minor arpeggio (two octaves)

Ab major scale (two octaves)

Ab major arpeggio (two octaves)

Dominant 7th in the key of Db, starting on Ab (two octaves)

G# melodic minor scale (two octaves)

G# harmonic minor scale (two octaves)

G# minor arpeggio (two octaves)

Grade 6 continued

All candidates should prepare the following:

D major scale in thumb position (one octave, starting on the D string)

Chromatic scale starting on C# (two octaves)

Chromatic scale starting on E♭ (two octaves)

Diminished 7th starting on C (two octaves)

Diminished 7th starting on E (two octaves)

Technical Exercise (from memory):

Double-stops (in sixths in C major):

or Section ii) Orchestral Excerpts. See Strings syllabus for details.

Grade 7

Candidate to prepare the Bowing Exercise and then *either* Section i) *or* Section ii) in full.

Bowing Exercise (from memory):

The candidate will be asked to play one scale of their own choice from any of those listed below for Grade 7. The whole scale should be played with hooked* bowing, as in the following example (♩ = 88):

etc.

Section i) Scales and Arpeggios and Technical Exercises (all from memory):

The candidate should prepare major and minor scales and arpeggios from Group 1 *or* Group 2. Additionally, **all** candidates should prepare thumb position scales, chromatic scales, diminished 7th arpeggios and technical exercises listed on pages 42-44.

When the examiner requests a major tonal centre, the candidate should play in succession:
> The major scale
> The major arpeggio
> The dominant 7th starting on that note and resolving onto the tonic (two octaves)

When the examiner requests a minor tonal centre, the candidate should play in succession:
> The melodic minor scale
> The harmonic minor scale
> The minor arpeggio

The candidate may pause briefly between individual scales and arpeggios.

All scales to be prepared with separate bows and slurred seven notes to a bow, as requested by the examiner, except for thumb position scales (to be prepared with separate bows and slurred four notes to a bow).

All arpeggios to be prepared with separate bows *and* slurred three notes to a bow.

Dominant 7ths to be prepared with separate bows *and* slurred four notes to a bow.

Diminished 7ths to be prepared with separate bows *and* slurred four notes to a bow.

Chromatic scales to be prepared with separate bows *and* slurred six notes to a bow.

See pages 2-4 for rhythmic and bowing patterns.

Group 1 – F, G, D♭/C♯ tonal centres:

F major scale (three octaves)

*Hooked bowing: this describes a method of bowing a repeated dotted quaver-semiquaver rhythm.

Grade 7 continued

F major arpeggio (three octaves)

Dominant 7th in the key of B♭, starting on F (two octaves)

F melodic minor scale (three octaves)

F harmonic minor scale (three octaves)

F minor arpeggio (three octaves)

G major scale (three octaves)

G major arpeggio (three octaves)

Dominant 7th in the key of C, starting on G (two octaves)

G melodic minor scale (three octaves)

G harmonic minor scale (three octaves)

Grade 7 continued

G minor arpeggio (three octaves)

Db major scale (three octaves)

Db major arpeggio (three octaves)

Dominant 7th in the key of Gb, starting on Db (two octaves)

C# melodic minor scale (three octaves)

C# harmonic minor scale (three octaves)

C# minor arpeggio (three octaves)

or

Group 2 – D, E, F# tonal centres:

D tonal centre (see Grade 6 pages 31–32)

E major scale (three octaves)

E major arpeggio (three octaves)

Grade 7 continued

Dominant 7th in the key of A, starting on E (two octaves)

E melodic minor scale (three octaves)

E harmonic minor scale (three octaves)

E minor arpeggio (three octaves)

F# major scale (three octaves)

F# major arpeggio (three octaves)

Dominant 7th in the key of B, starting on F# (two octaves)

F# melodic minor scale (three octaves)

F# harmonic minor scale (three octaves)

F# minor arpeggio (three octaves)

Grade 7 continued

All candidates should prepare the following:

Diminished 7th starting on F (two octaves)

Diminished 7th starting on F♯ (two octaves)

D major scale in thumb position (one octave)

D major arpeggio in thumb position (one octave)

D melodic minor scale in thumb position (one octave)

D harmonic minor scale in thumb position (one octave)

D minor arpeggio in thumb position (one octave)

Chromatic scale starting on E (two octaves)

Chromatic scale starting on Db (two octaves)

Technical Exercises (from memory):

Double Stops

a) C major in sixths (one octave, in the following pattern):

($\quarternote$ = 120)

Grade 7 continued

b) B♭ major in thirds (one octave):

or Section ii) Orchestral Excerpts. See Strings syllabus for details.

Grade 8

Candidate to prepare the Bowing Exercise and then *either* Section i) *or* Section ii) in full.

Bowing Exercise (from memory):

The candidate will be asked to play one scale of their own choice from any of those listed below for Grade 8. The examiner will choose any **one** of the specified bowings from Grade 5, 6 or 7 and ask the candidate to play their scale with that bowing.

Section i) Scales and Arpeggios and Technical Exercises (all from memory):

The candidate should prepare major and minor scales and arpeggios from Group 1 *or* Group 2. Additionally, candidates should prepare chromatic scales and diminished 7th arpeggios from their chosen groups, and technical exercises, listed on pages 52-56.

When the examiner requests a major tonal centre, the candidate should play in succession:
> The major scale
> The major arpeggio
> The dominant 7th starting on that note and resolving onto the tonic (two octaves)

When the examiner requests a minor tonal centre, the candidate should play in succession:
> The melodic minor scale
> The harmonic minor scale
> The minor arpeggio

The candidate may pause briefly between individual scales and arpeggios.

All scales to be prepared with separate bows *and* slurred seven notes to a bow.

All arpeggios to be prepared with separate bows *and* slurred three notes to a bow.

Dominant 7ths to be prepared with separate bows *and* slurred four notes to a bow.

Chromatic scales (starting on each of the four notes of the chosen group) to be prepared with separate bows *and* slurred twelve notes to a bow.

Diminished 7ths (starting on each of the four notes of the chosen group) to be prepared with separate bows *and* slurred four notes to a bow.

See pages 2-4 for rhythmic and bowing patterns.

Group 1 – A, F♯, B♭, D♭/C♯ tonal centres:

A major scale (three octaves)

A major arpeggio (three octaves)

Grade 8 continued

Dominant 7th in the key of D, starting on A (two octaves)

A melodic minor scale (three octaves)

A harmonic minor scale (three octaves)

A minor arpeggio (three octaves)

F# major scale (three octaves)

F# major arpeggio (three octaves)

Dominant 7th in the key of B, starting on F# (two octaves)

F# melodic minor scale (three octaves)

F# harmonic minor scale (three octaves)

F# minor arpeggio (three octaves)

Grade 8 continued

Bb major scale (three octaves)

Bb major arpeggio (three octaves)

Dominant 7th in the key of Eb, starting on Bb (two octaves)

Bb melodic minor scale (three octaves)

Bb harmonic minor scale (three octaves)

B♭ minor arpeggio (three octaves)

D♭ major scale (three octaves)

D♭ major arpeggio (three octaves)

Dominant 7th in the key of G♭, starting on D♭ (two octaves)

C# melodic minor scale (three octaves)

Grade 8 continued

C# harmonic minor scale (three octaves)

C# minor arpeggio (three octaves)

or

Group 2 – G, B♭, E♭, A♭/G# tonal centres:

G tonal centre (see Grade 7 pages 37–38)

B♭ tonal centre (see Grade 8 pages 48–49)

E♭ major scale (three octaves)

E♭ major arpeggio (three octaves)

Dominant 7th in the key of A♭, starting on E♭ (two octaves)